VOLUME 1

Tuneful Graded Studies

Arranged by
DOROTHY BRADLEY

FOREWORD

The first volume of the series of *Tuneful Graded Studies*, which are important are selected from the works of standard composers, covers the most importantground in the early stages of piano technics:- Formation of a good position of the hand and fingers from the simplest five-finger group to more extended positions; finger individualisation; steady, even tone in legato playing; finger wrist staccato; very simple chord-playing for forearm touch; aid to time perception by gradual introduction of different note-values,rests and easy subdivisions of the beat. A few new, original studies are included.

Tempo indications are intended as general guidance to what may be expected of a young beginner. Where two sets of figures are given the first should be regarded as the lowest at which the study (after practise) should be taken for good rhythmic effect.

The last few studies in the volume combine or amplify features introduced in the earlier and easier ones.

D.B.

BOSWORTH
14-15 Berners Street,
London W1T 3LJ, UK.

CONTENTS

			Page
1.	For Even Time and Tone, Five-Finger Position	D.B.	3
2.	Steady Timing, Semibreve Rest	BURGMULLER.	3
3.	Independent Movement Between the Hands	D.B.	4
4.	More L.H. Work	D.B.	4
5.	Simple Phrasing	D.B.	4
6.	Triple Time, Introduces Crotchet Rest	KOHLER.	4
7.	Steady Rhythm, Legato, Chord Shapes	KOHLER.	5
8.	Different Intervals Built Upon Chords	KOHLER.	5
9.	Staccato Exercise, Precision of Beat	BURGMULLER.	6
10.	Both Hands Play a Tune	D.B.	6
11.	More Detailed Phrasing, L.H. Part on Chord of C.	CZERNY.	7
12.	Changing Intervals, Rhythmic Steadiness	D.B.	7
13.	Fingerwork for Both Hands	D.B.	8
14.	Staccato and Legato Single Notes, Sustained Bass	D.B.	8
14a.	Staccato Thirds for Wrist Touch	BURGMULLER.	9
15.	Touch Contrasts, Phrasing, Entering on the Weak Beat	BURGMULLER.	9
16.	Singing Touch, Tone Control for Both Hands	BURGMULLER.	10
17.	Finger Independence and Touch Changes	CZERNY.	10
18.	Single Notes in Chord Shapes Against Small Firm Chords	CZERNY.	11
19.	Couplets of Slurred Notes	BURGMULLER.	11
20.	Slurred and Staccato Melody, Small Broken Chord Accompaniment	KOHLER.	12
21.	Slurred Couplets With More Detail, Minim and Crotchet Rests	BURGMULLER.	12
22.	Slurs From Weak to Strong	BURGMULLER.	13
23.	Similar, with Hands In Unison and Contrary Movement	BURGMULLER.	13
24.	Contrasts in Touch and Tone, Introduces One Flat	CZERNY.	14
25.	Single Staccato Notes for Both Hands, Bright Tone, Steady Rhythm	CZERNY.	14
26.	Beat Precision and Finger Development	CZERNY.	15
27.	Flowing Rhythm, Legato, Tone Control, Phrasing	D.B.	16
28.	Evenness in Timing Notes and Rests, Introduces One Sharp	KOHLER.	17
29.	For Steadiness in Triplets	BURGMULLER.	18
30.	Tone Control in Quiet Melody and Accompaniment	D.B.	18
31.	Details of Touch in Small Phrases, Introduces Two Sharps	CZERNY.	19
32.	Melody Playing, Contractions, Thumb Under Finger	KOHLER.	20
33.	The Same Melody With Variations	KOHLER.	20
34.	Dotted Crotchet and Quaver Above Steady Broken Chords	D.B.	21
35.	Staccato Broken Chords Above Sustained Bass	D.B.	22
36.	Legato and Staccato Against Smooth Notes	D.B.	22
37.	Crisp Finger and Wrist Work, L.H.Detail	CZERNY.	23
38.	Sustained Tone in Small Chords	CZERNY.	23
39.	Finger Agility for Right Hand	CZERNY.	24
40.	Expressive Melody, Phrasing	Le COUPPEY.	25
41.	Melody for R.H. and L.H. Against Small Chords	BRUNNER.	26
42.	Legato Thirds, Rhythmic Movement	CZERNY.	27
43.	For Evenness and Tone Control	KOHLER.	28
44.	Clear Fingerwork for R.H. Touch Changes	D.B.	29
45.	For Daintiness and Beat Precision	D.B.	30
46.	Staccato and Legato Thirds Against Single Notes	BURGMULLER.	31
47.	Bright Accents, Movement of Weak to Strong	KOHLER.	31
48.	Timing of Tied Notes, Graceful Style	Le COUPPEY.	32
49.	Broken Chords Divided Between the Hands	D.B..	33
50.	Slurred and Staccato Melody Above Steady Accompaniment	MULLER.	34
51.	Rhythmic Steadiness in Notes of Different Values	MULLER.	35
52.	Cantabile Touch, Tone Contrasts	Le COUPPEY.	36
53.	Clean Attack, Neat Touch Changes	Le COUPPEY.	37
54.	Melody, Phrasing, Legato Accompaniment in Broken Chords	Le COUPPEY.	38
55.	Melody in Both Hands	LOESCHHORN.	40

June 28/9

B.&Co.Ltd.19645

TUNEFUL GRADED STUDIES
(Various Composers)

The first five little preparatory Studies should be played at a very easy pace, and great care should be taken with the movement of each finger and the smooth connection of the sounds. Prepare the hands over the five keys and keep the finger tips firm as the keys go down.

For Even Time and Tone, Five-Finger Position

See that the keys in both hands go down exactly together.

D. B.

For Steady Timing, Semibreve Rest

BURGMULLER

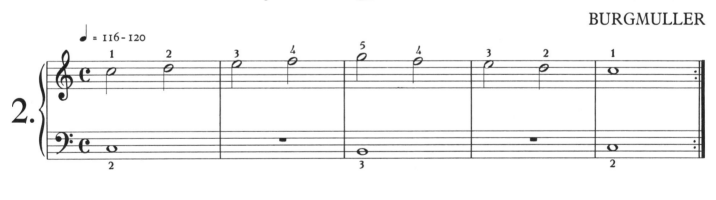

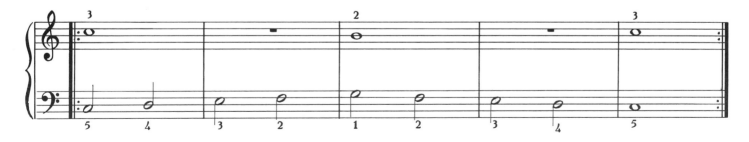

B.&Co.Ltd. 19645

Tous droits d'exécution réservés
Made in England

Independent Movement Between the Hands

D. B.

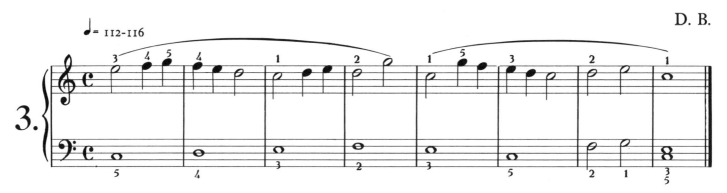

More Left Hand Work

D. B.

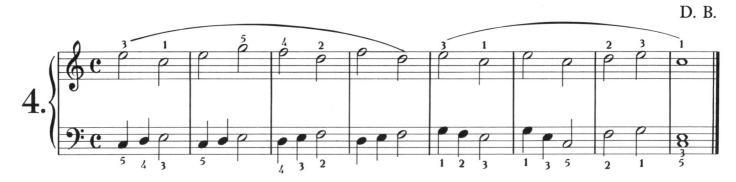

Simple Phrasing

Try for nice tone in both hands.   Make a break at the end of the slur to give the
music a breathing space.

D. B.

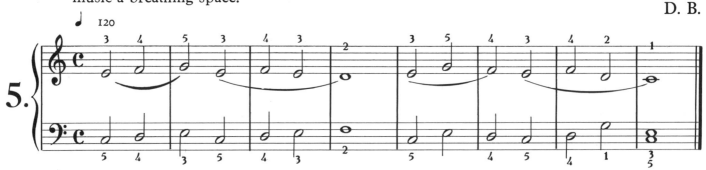

Triple Time, Introduces Crotchet Rest

See that the third beat of each bar progresses easily to the first beat of next bar.
Aim for nice bright tone.

KOHLER

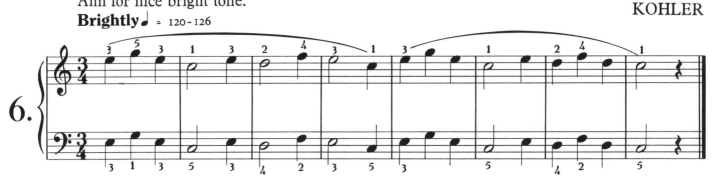

B. & Co. Ltd. 19645

Steady Rhythm, Legato, Chord Shapes

KOHLER

7.

Different Intervals Built Upon Chords

Make sure that each hand knows its part before joining them together. Shape the R.H. over the first three notes before beginning to play.

KOHLER

8.

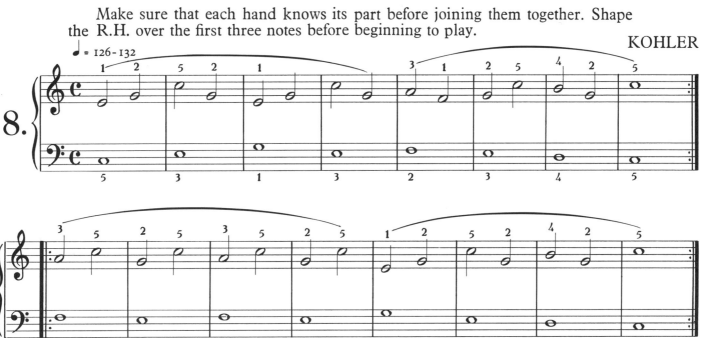

Staccato Exercise, Precision of Beat

For the repeated staccato notes keep the finger tip firm, get the movement from the wrist. Give the key a little 'kick' and then at once give up and let the key 'kick' back.

BURGMULLER

Both Hands Play a Tune

Try for good singing tone in both hands. Attend to the phrasing.

D. B.

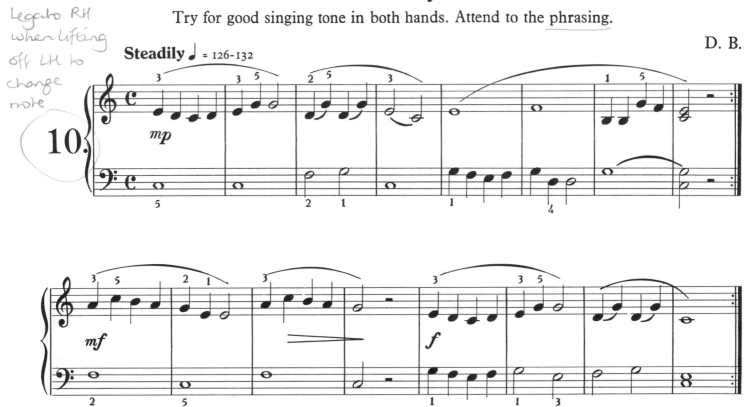

More Detailed Phrasing,
Left Hand Part Built on the Chord of C.

Tone of *R.H.* should be bright; *L.H.* firm and sustained.

CZERNY

legato RH

11.

Changing Intervals, Rhythmic Steadiness

Be mindful of legato RH when lifting LH

Keep a very steady beat and make the music seem to move forward brightly. Make the changing notes in bars 5 to 7 and 9 to 11 stronger than the others—more singing in quality.

D. B.

Moderato ♩ = 126

mf

12.

Fingerwork for Both Hands, Legato and Staccato

Play with a well-arched hand in order to give strength to the fingers.   Be careful
to change the touch from *legato* to *staccato* as shown, and use finger action for both.

D. B.

Staccato and Legato Single Notes,
Sustained Bass, Tone Gradations

Use wrist action with firm fingers for the repeated staccato notes. Make the L.H.
dotted minims sing clearly, and attend to tone gradations, and to forward movement
from weak beats too strong.

D. B.

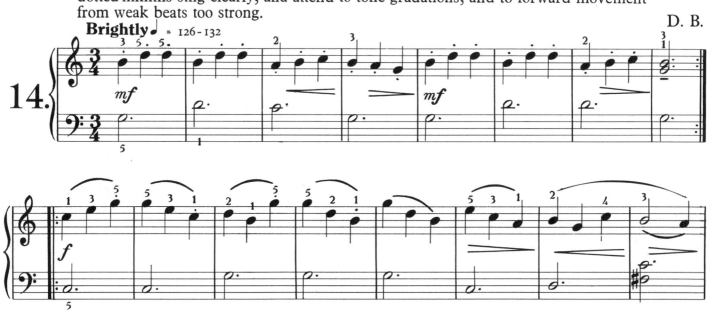

B.&Co.Ltd.19645

Staccato Thirds for Wrist Touch

Prepare each set of fingers for their notes; keep the finger tips firm; play from the wrist, and let the keys come up the instant the sound is made. Begin to practise *very slowly*.

BURGMULLER

14a.

Touch Contrasts, Phrasing, Entering on the Weak Beat

As the first two notes come in before the bar-line, be sure to make them quiet enough to be able to bring out the following accent without bumping it. Attend to all touch changes. Try for a bright, cheerful effect.

BURGMULLER

15.

10

Singing Touch, Tone Control for Both Hands

The melody, whichever hand plays it, must have sweetly singing tone, with careful grading of tone from soft to only moderately loud. The semibreves must be clear and well-sustained.

BURGMULLER

Finger Independence and Touch Changes
(Work for the Weaker Fingers)

Steady time and bright tone needed throughout, with special attention to 'turning corners' in bars 4, 6, 8. etc.

CZERNY

B. & Co. Ltd. 19645

Single Notes in Chord Shapes Against Small Firm Chords

Notice that, although in single notes, the R.H. part is built on chord shapes, and prepare the fingers over these before beginning to play. See that the quavers move smoothly to the first staccato note. The staccato notes to be played with wrist touch. Make sure that the L.H. notes of chords sound exactly together.

CZERNY

Couplets of Slurred Notes

The first of each two notes must be played with an accent, by a down movement of the forearm; the second played lightly and softly, by an up movement. Think "Down, Up." for each group.

BURGMULLER

B.&Co.Ltd.19645

Slurred and Staccato Melody,
Small Broken Chord Accompaniment

Similar features to No. 19 but brisker in movement.   The staccato notes must be tossed off lightly from the wrist, and the third quaver must be lighter than the second. See that L.H. accompaniment is not too loud and that it comes in exactly with R.H.; but smoothly all through.

KOHLER

20.

Slurred Couplets With More Detail

Care must be taken with the exact timing of notes and rests against the slurred and staccato figures.

BURGMULLER

21.

B. & Co. Ltd. 19645

Slurs From Weak to Strong

Here the slur is used with quite different meaning from that in the previous studies.
Now it is just a *legato* slur leading from a *weak* to a *strong* beat. Let the accented
staccato notes be bright.

BURGMULLER

22.

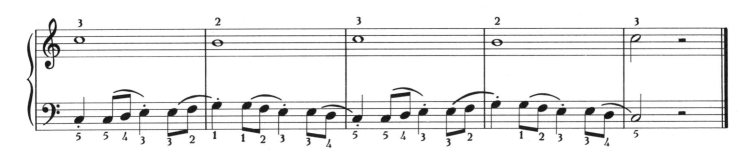

Slurs From Weak to Strong,
Hands In Unison and Contrary Movement

Similar to No. 22, but now the hands play together. Practise slowly until everything
goes easily.

BURGMULLER

23.

B.&Co.Ltd.19645

Contrasts in Touch and Tone

(Introduces One Flat)

CZERNY

24.

Single Staccato Notes for Both Hands, for Bright Tone and Steady Rhythm

CZERNY

25.

B.& Co.Ltd.19645

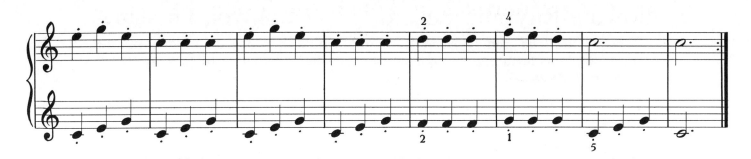

For Beat Precision and Finger Development

To be played with bright tone throughout. Time the notes of both hands to go down exactly together. Play the repeated staccato notes with wrist movement and make the fingers 'stand up for themselves'.

CZERNY

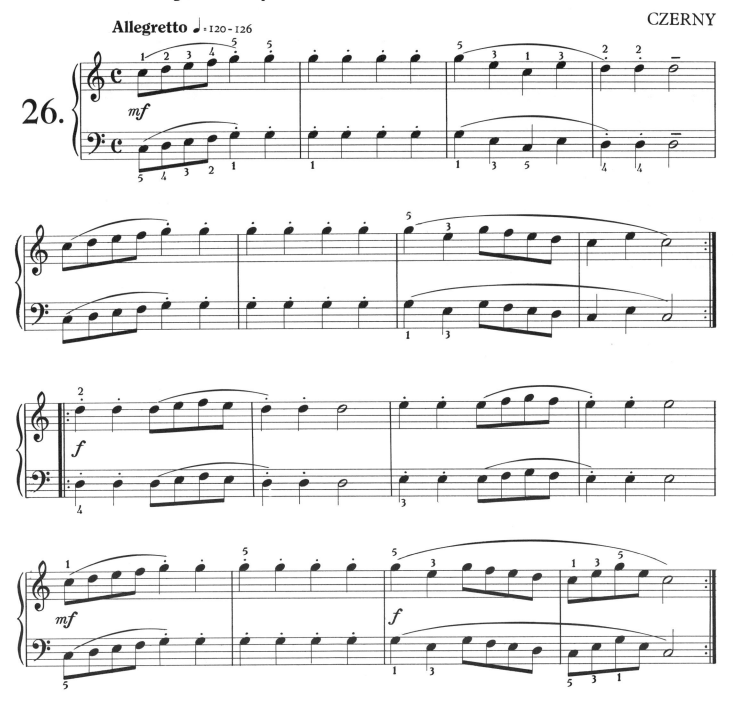

B.&Co.Ltd.19645

Flowing Rhythm, Legato, Tone Control, Phrasing

Phrasing and tone grading are most important here. Play the dotted minims with enough tone to let them sing through the bar. Constantly think of the forward movement of *weak* to *strong* beats.

D. B.

For Evenness in Timing Notes and Rests

Remember that RESTS stand for SILENCE in the part in which they occur, so be careful to come away from the keys at the right instant of time.

KOHLER

Allegretto ♩ = 126

28.

legato

For Steadiness in Triplets

The best way to play triplets evenly is to use the 'Time-names' *Ta-te-ti* for each group, and make the *Ta-te-tis* move forward without the least gap between. See that the second and third notes of each group are softer than the first, and make these softer notes lead straight into the *following first note*.

BURGMULLER

Tone Control in Quiet Melody and Accompaniment

Similar in style to No. 27, but this melody is gentle throughout, and the *crescendos* and *diminuendos* must be within a small range of tone.

B.&Co.Ltd.19645

Details of Touch in Small Phrase Groups
Introduces Two Sharps

Notice that this Study is built upon the chord of D Major in both parts.   Before playing prepare the hands over their chords ("a" "b") with middle finger over F sharp, so that all the notes can be played without any awkard movement. Originally in the key of C, transposed for the sake of variety.

CZERNY

B.&Co.Ltd.19645

For Melody Playing, Contractions, Thumb Under Finger and Finger over Thumb

Care should be taken in bars 6-7, L.H., and 12-13-14, R.H. in order to turn finger over thumb or thumb under finger with perfect smoothness; also in bars 7 (L.H.) and 15 (R.H.) where the fingers must be prepared for closer positions of the notes.

KOHLER

The Same Melody With Variations

See that the melody stands out above the ornamental notes.   Keep steady rhythm throughout. Transposed from key of C.

KOHLER

B.&Co.Ltd.19645

For Timing the Dotted Crotchet and Quaver
Above Steady Broken Chords

Although the quaver belongs to the same beat as the dot, think of it as really con-
nected musically with the next note.   Also play the quaver more softly than either
the dotted crotchet or the crotchet which follows it.

D. B.

Staccato Broken Chords, R.H., Above Sustained Bass

The right hand and forearm should neatly be adjusted to enable the fingers to reach their keys.

D. B.

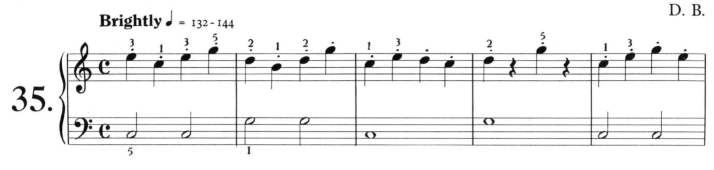

Legato and Staccato Against Smooth Notes

Attend to small details of touch shown by small slurs and staccato marks. The long slurs are phrase marks.

D. B.

Crisp Finger and Wrist Work, Left Hand Detail

Try for good tone variants and general brightness,
with very steady time.

CZERNY

Sustained Tone in Small Chords

Forearm Touch

For the small chords fingers and hands should be arched and firm, fingers prepared
over their keys, movement from the forearm.

CZERNY

Finger Agility for Right Hand

Think each group of semiquavers forward to the next accent.   Keep the fingers
nicely curved, tips firm.   Try for really good finger action.

CZERNY

Expressive Melody, Phrasing

Attend to the small slurs (see No.19) and rests. The long slurs show the phrase movement of the music. Keep the L.H. accompaniment quiet, but give character and warm tone to the first note of each bar.

Le COUPPEY

Melody for Right Hand and Left Hand Against Small Chords

It is a good plan to play the tune by itself, first in one hand and then the other until its outline has been grasped. When the chords are added see that they are quieter than the melody, especially when they come in the R.H.

BRUNNER

41.

Legato Thirds, Rhythmic Movement

A well-arched hand ready to back up the fingers, and firm fingers to carry through, are necessary for this. Feel that the weight is transferred from one set of fingers to the next.   Aim for graceful, flowing rhythm.

CZERNY

For Evenness and Tone Control

Be sure to keep the time of the quavers perfectly even.

KOHLER

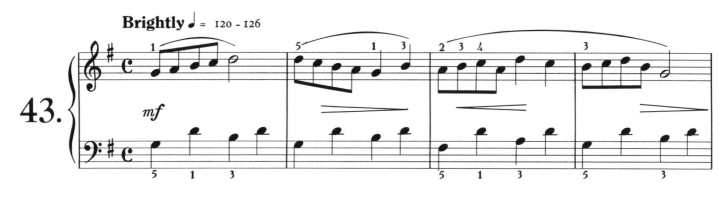

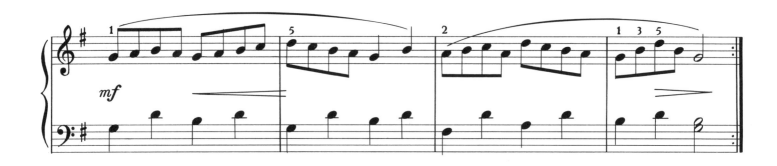

Clear Fingerwork for R.H., Against Small Chords
(Touch Changes)

Attend to every mark of *staccato* and *legato*. Make sure that the semiquavers run
without the slightest break into the following quaver, and then "kick off".

D. B.

For Daintiness and Beat Precision

This needs a strict beat, and neat playing. The repeated staccato notes and L.H. small chords should be played with wrist touch, single moving notes with finger touch.

D. B.

Staccato and Legato Thirds Against Single Notes

Right hand must be the more prominent in the first half, and L.H. in the second half of this Study.   The single minims etc. should sing quietly.

BURGMULLER

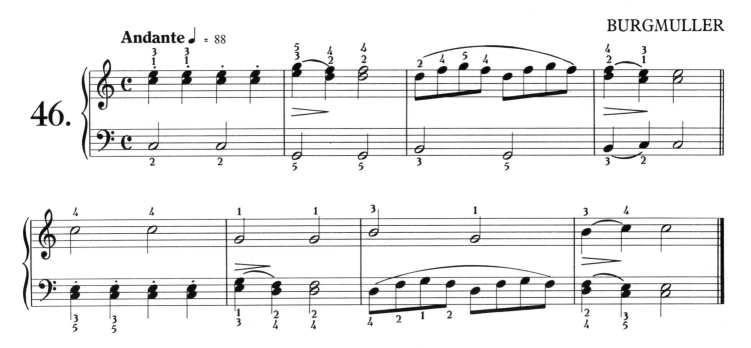

Bright Accents, Movement of Weak to Strong

Take care that the notes before the bar-lines are really quiet and that they move easily forward to the accented notes.   Keep a briskly steady beat.

KOHLER

32

For Timing of Tied Notes, Graceful Style

Le COUPPEY

Broken Chords Divided Between the Hands

First prepare the hands over each of the chords, as shown in No. 31, make quite sure of grouping of notes and fingers.   Then, when playing as written, see that there is no break between L.H. and R.H. notes.

D. B.

Slurred and Staccato Melody Above Steady Accompaniment

Left hand should practise alone a good deal until the notes are quite well known;
then they can move along evenly to form a nicely coloured background for the melody.
R.H. must attend to all small details.

MULLER

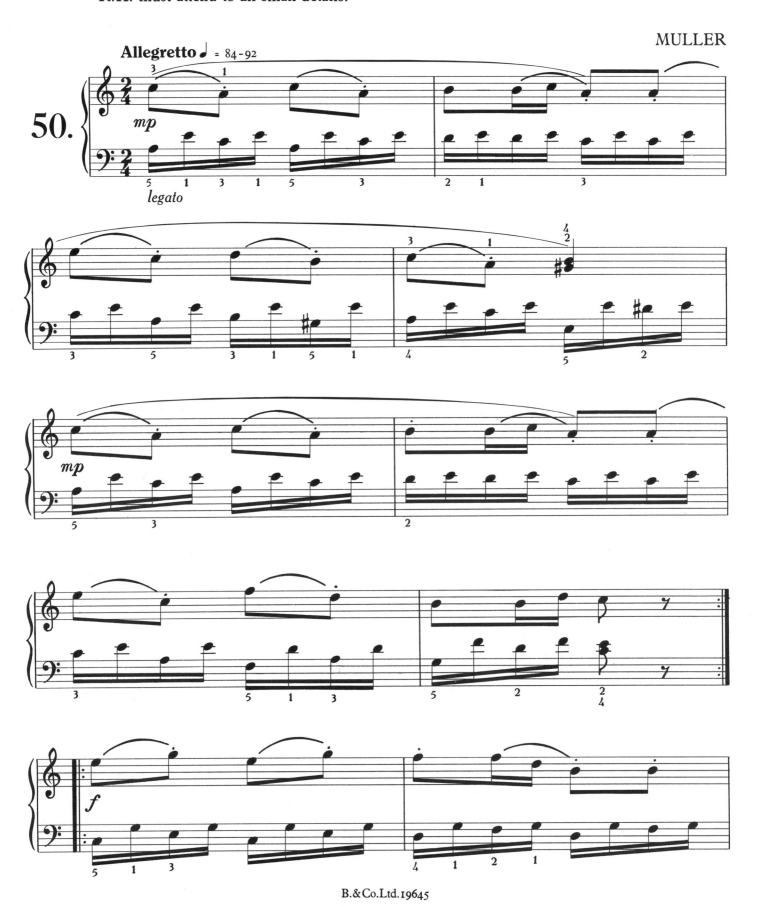

For Rhythmic Steadiness in Notes of Different Values

The point requiring care is to enter with the R.H. quavers exactly on the fourth beat, and let them flow evenly to the next beat. Play the dotted minims with good tone so that they sing for their proper time value.

MULLER

Andante con espressione ♩ = 104-108

51.

Cantabile Touch, Tone Contrasts

Whichever hand has the melody must sing out above the other. Sometimes—as in bars 5 to 8 and 13 to 20—both hands have melody and they must sing together, though here L.H. should be a little stronger than R.H.

Le COUPPEY

For Clean Attack, Neat Touch Changes

Le COUPPEY

Melody, Phrasing, Legato Accompaniment
in Small Broken Chords

Le COUPPEY

Melody in Both Hands

LOESCHHORN

Printed and bound in Great Britain by
Caligraving Limited Thetford Norfolk

B.&Co.Ltd.19645

8/07(63220)